Happy Centennial Saskatchewan

My Set-up at Emma Lake, 46 cm × 61 cm (18" × 24")

Happy Centennial Saskatchewan

Poetry by DAVID BOUCHARD

Paintings by HANS HEROLD

Simple Truth Publications Inc.
Regina

Cold Bald October Prairie: 1840, 46 cm × 61 cm (18" × 24")

I can see the black cloud coming

I can hear my brother call

Feel the earth still all around me

As the snow begins to fall

And the ground begins to rumble

And my heart pounds hard within

I can see the black cloud coming

The new hunt will soon begin.

I was brought up from Montana
Asked to come back north and help
Asked to leave my home and family
Told the Metis needed help
In the North West – more injustice
To my people – red and white
I came back to help my brother
I did not come home to fight.

As it was in Manitoba
There were men who came and took
With no thought of those who lived here
They just came out west and took –
First the buffalo – then our rivers
First our food and then our pride
I came back up to the North West
Where they tried me – where I died.

Cemetery at Batoche: 1885, 46 cm × 61 cm (18" × 24")

Mud Shack: 1899, 46 cm × 61 cm (18" × 24")

I went to Southern Africa
To fight a man I did not know
My Queen said that she needed me
I told the wife I had to go…
What made this war so different
Was that I was asked to bring with me
My fastest horse – my trusted steed
What did my country want of me?

It seemed that I had gone to fight
A Dutchman known down there as "Boer"
Whose way of making war was new
Old England had not seen before.
They'd ride in fast on horseback, STRIKE
Then turn and run from whence they came
But we, Canadian Roughriders
Would save the day and earn our name.

The west had a strange grip on me
The lure of wild and dangerous land
And I a man of destiny
I'd head out west and lend a hand.
The railway would soon follow me
And who to better set the scene
I'd scout and find the perfect place
I'd buy that land and lay my dream.

I told him there was ample water
Wood abundant – all he'd need
The CP should pass right through here
I'd found the place – I'd sown the seed.
The locals called it Pile of Bones
But names out here were all being changed
My friend, MacDonald trusted me
And thus Regina came to fame.

Saskatchewan's Legislature, 46 cm × 61 cm (18" × 24")

This drought will surely come to pass
This wind...this sun...this raging dust
These damned grasshoppers right from hell
No sign of rain yet in God we trust.

Month to month and year to year
Our farmlands have been blown away
By wind and sun and never ending dust
Our homeland has been blown away.

And yet I thank God every day
For my wife and kids, the farm and the team.
To not count one's blessings just wouldn't be right
I thank God every day he allows me to dream.

———

The Depression: 1930, 46 cm × 61 cm (18" × 24")

You'll find me on the prairie
Not the north – the southern prairie
Rising high above a wheat field
Standing strong in blowing snow drifts
Towering proud through drought and famine
Always there – through drought and famine.

But my days seem to be numbered
As the landscape here is changing.
I'm being taken down board by board
No more needed – board by board
Sold for salvage – board by board
The landscape here is changing.

Vanishing landmarks, 46 cm × 61 cm (18" × 24")

Prairie folk have time to think
Through cold, dark winters – sit and think
We picture how the world could be
A better place for you and for me.

We out here use common sense
We think of things that make good sense
To eat and sleep, to fight the cold
Care for our young, our sick, and our old.

And when I dreamt up Medicare
I hoped, though I was not aware
That others would soon come to see
The gift of caring and sometimes think of me.

Old Saskatoon Hospital – Tommy's Legacy, 46 cm × 61 cm (18" × 24")

I'm home to wolf and mountain cat
Northern Pike and Rainbow Trout
Bear and Moose and Deer and Fox
Badgers too – though not a lot.

I'm home to Cree and the Metis
Whom I have nurtured here for years
Then white man came and chose to stay
I've heard him laugh and I've dried his tears.

A million trees and cold, dark lakes
Seen clear by raven's watchful eye
Clean rivers wild run everywhere
I am the North – both earth and sky.

Beautiful Northern Saskatchewan, 46 cm × 61 cm (18" × 24")

We came west by tens of thousands
Left our families and our homes
All this land was free for taking
We could make this place our own.

We were Ukraines – we were Dutch
Most of Norway, so it seemed
Many came from the Slovakias
We all came with the same dream.

We were Germans – we were Poles
Most were young though some were old
Others came from mother Russia
"Free and good land," we'd been told.

With traditions and with cultures
Languages we'd not forsake
With religions, foods and dances
These vast prairies – here to take.

Ukrainian Church – Krydor, Saskatchewan, 46 cm × 61 cm (18" × 24")

I had stopped to rest along a lake

Fatigued from days of fighting.

I had lay to rest along a lake

When first I heard her calling.

"Who's calling?" I cried – I know your voice

It was she – my true love who was calling.

"Qui Appelle" I cried out when I heard her again

There was something so wrong – "I am coming!"

I've ridden and paddled all of these lakes

Over decades I've searched for my lover.

I've called out for her – again and again

And I will till such time that I find her.

Qu'Appelle, 46 cm × 61 cm (18" × 24")

Saskatchewan Winter, 46 cm × 61 cm (18" × 24")

You can't think of Saskatchewan
Without thinking of winter
How hard life must have been back then
In sod huts during those long hard months
Of bitter cold and blowing winds
Thick ice on every pond and lake
We'd never try to celebrate
Without thinking of winter.

We're just as proud as any
When we speak about our history
The birthplace of the Mounties
The Great War – the Depression
Yet another war and Medicare
Two Grey Cups and much, much more
Yet ask us what Saskatchewan is
And *we'll* all say, *"It's winter"*.

We children of Saskatchewan
Are easy to identify
We smile at strangers – stop to talk
To people we know nothing of…
We open up our hearts and homes
To all who might come knocking
We're what we are – because of you
Because of you, Saskatchewan.

Happy Birthday dear Saskatchewan
From the seeds that you have sown
Though we've left for far off places
We still think of you as home.
And Happy Birthday dear Saskatchewan
From your children who have stayed
You have always and will always
Be here for us – as we'd prayed.

Happy Birthday Saskatchewan, 46 cm × 61 cm (18" × 24")

I too count all my blessings
God has given me my share and more
Oil and potash, lakes and trees
I've so much to be thankful for
And with your help I have the task
Of feeding countless sick and poor
The breadbasket of all the world
A small opening to heaven's door.

Like mothers the world over
I am proud of all my children
The Cree, Blackfoot, Assiniboian,
Riel and Tommy Douglas,
John Diefenbaker, Dewdney,
Sandra Schmirler – all of you
You've made Saskatchewan very proud
On this my 100th birthday.

The Breadbasket, 46 cm × 61 cm (18" × 24")

Note From The Publisher

John Kurtz

What do W. O. Mitchell and David Bouchard have in common? They are the only two Saskatchewan authors listed on *Maclean's* magazine's list of the twenty top children's books in the history of Canada.

What *Maclean's* might have missed did not escape the attention of Toronto Public Librarian, *Theo Hersh:* "This is a book that is hard to put down and easy to return to. Is it an adult book masquerading as a children's book? A child will be drawn in by the poetry's ingenious metaphors. An adult will hear the nostalgic echoes of childhood."

We, from Canada's three prairie provinces, have claimed David's sentiments as our own, but his heartfelt memories and poetry run deeper and further than our borders. The U.S. makes claims that are not all that unfounded. *Atheneum Books for Young Readers* wrote: "No matter what region of the country we come from, a sense of the prairie, symbolizing the endurance of the American spirit, rests in our hearts. *If You're Not From The Prairie* elicits those feelings and appeals as a celebration of American pride."

In her review for the Weekend Sun, Janet Collins wrote: "The well-known author of *The Elders Are Watching* is a resident of North Vancouver but grew up in Saskatchewan and has found part of that life still with him."

David has not found "part of that life still with him." He is more than that…

His hair is mostly wind, his eyes are filled with grit
His skin is white or brown; his lips are chapped and split
He has lain on the prairie and heard grasses sigh
He has stared at the vast open bowl in the sky
He has seen every castle and face in the clouds
His home is the prairie and for that he is proud…

If you're not from the prairie, you can't know his soul
You don't know his blizzards, you've not fought his cold
You can't know his mind, nor even his heart
Unless deep within you, there's somehow a part
A part of the things that he said that he knows
The wind, sky, the earth, the storms and the cold
But say that you have, and then you'll be one
For you will have shared that same blazing sun.

There was little question whom I would ask to write this tribute to our province, on this our one hundredth birthday. David has coined the image of what it is to be Prairie born. He is a poet, a writer, a teacher and a champion of literacy. He has written two books on reading and spends much of his life touring the globe in the hopes of making reading something to be attainable to all—not just a few fortunate souls.

What David Bouchard has put into words Hans Herold has captured on canvas. From the sun covered fields of grain on the prairies to the glistening clear lakes in the north, Hans Herold has documented what a wonderful province we live in. Although Hans Herold has painted thousands of scenes, he never ceases to see new beauty and historical significance and this ability formed a partnership with one of Canada's great storytellers. The love of Hans Herold for his adopted country inspired him to make a heartfelt contribution in the celebration of Saskatchewan's Centennial.

Author

Saskatchewan born **David Bouchard** is the author of over two dozen books. His books have won several prestigious awards, among them: the Lee Bennet Hopkins Poetry Award for *Voices from the Wild*, the Red Cedar Award for *The Great Race*, the Amelia Frances Howard-Gibbon Award for *The Dragon New Year* and the Governor-General's Award for *The Song Within My Heart*. His books have been short-listed many times for several of Canada's most outstanding awards, among them: the Mr. Christie Award for *The Great Race*, the Governor General's Award for *The Great Race* and for *The Dragon New Year*, the Shelia A. Egoff Children's Book Prize for *If You're Not From The Prairie*, *Voices From The Wild*, *If Sarah Will Take Me* and for *A Barnyard Bestiary*, the Hackamattack Award and the Rocky Mountain Award.

If You're Not From The Prairie is listed on Maclean's list of the top twenty children's books in the history of Canada. *If You're Not From The Prairie*, *Qu'Appelle*, and *The Song Within My Heart* all appear on a list of the 25 Canadian Children's Classics published by Southam News.

David is one of Canada's most sought-after public speakers. He has presented to hundreds of thousands of educators, parents and students throughout the world. Through his keynotes and presentations he champions literacy. He defines the roles and responsibilities of educators and parents in providing children with *The Gift Of Reading*.

David is married to Vicki and their combined family totals five: Adrien, Etienne, Todd, Ashleigh and their own Victoria.

Artist

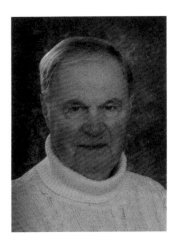

Hans Herold is a tall, intense man with piercing blue eyes. He was born in 1923 on the family's 200 year-old farm in the Bavarian Alps. Following the death of his parents he sold the farm and studied art in Munich, Germany, under Professor Maxon. Hans came to Saskatchewan in 1957 and found employment on a farm. Later he took a job as a miner in Uranium City. He would eventually return to Saskatoon where he made a living as a house painter. His goal, however, was to make a living painting landscapes. The early 1960's were a difficult time to sell original paintings in Saskatoon but in 1965 he had his first one-man show at the Mendel Art Gallery. From that successful show he continued to have exhibitions throughout Canada. In an article on Hans Herold in *Emerging Arts West*, Mark Lowey wrote: "Hans Herold has great respect for nature in its richness and unending mystery. He explores extremely varying moods, forms, textures. designs, and colour concepts. Each painting is a total separate expression."

Herold's works are widely held by Saskatchewan people and collectors throughout Canada. A talented prolific artist he has made an outstanding contribution to the art history of his adopted province.

Typesetting and layout by National Print-It Centres / Marlene Solberg

Simple Truth Publications
2861 23rd Ave.
Regina, SK   S4S 1E7

Simple Truth Publications Inc. is pleased to welcome the *Leader-Post* and the *Star-Phoenix* as a partner in the publication of *Happy Centennial Saskatchewan*, author David Bouchard, artist Hans Herold.

CanWest

 The "Raise-a-Reader" program will share in proceeds from the sale of the book, *Happy Centennial Saskatchewan*.

"Raise-a-Reader" is an award winning national campaign that promotes reading to children at an early age, setting the groundwork for a lifetime of literacy skills and a healthy interest in reading. The objectives of the Raise-a-Reader campaign are to encourage families to read together and to raise funds and resources for family literacy programs and organizations. Proceeds from the sale of this book will support Raise-a-Reader programs in Saskatchewan.

Printed and bound in Canada by
Friesens, Altona, Manitoba

ISBN 0-9733500-1-6

Dedication

For my little girl Victoria.
Darling, I have written you previously about why I am what I am.

> And several thousand miles away
> Your dad was warm and cared for
> By your grandma and your grandpa
> In a small, French, Catholic town.
> On the prairie – harsh and baron
> A small village in Saskatchewan
> Whose memories are of priests and snow
> Books, pianos, priests, and snow.
>
> I hope to take you there one day
> So you might better understand
> What made your dad just what he was
> What makes you think the way you do.
> I hope to take you there one day
> So you might see what kind of man
> Comes from one whose memories stem
> From books, pianos, priests and snow.

Sweet Victoria, this is for you…that you might better understand my
home and thus me.
                                                    —Daddy

I am grateful to my wife Heidi and my many friends in Saskatchewan who have shown so much love in making the many years spent living on the Prairies happy and rewarding.
                                                    —Hans Herold

We have many "Treasured Moments" stored up in our memories during the forty years we were so thankful to have our son James with us. "When I think of James I picture him as a "Prairie Spirit," free as the wind, soft as a new-fallen rain, and shining as brightly as a beautiful prairie sunset. He lived the "Prairie Spirit" as well, walking briskly and confidently to work in all kinds of weather – winter or summer.
                                                    —Monica and John Kurtz